For Conor and Sadhbh
ED and JG

For Kate Janaki (Ella) and Dara Luca
SK

James - the facts

James appears to have been a common name from ancient times. It may be derived from the Latin Jacomus or Hebrew Jacob, meaning supplanter.

The name has become one of the most widespread in western Europe and has developed variations in the British Isles such as Seamus (Ireland), Hamish (Scotland), Iago (Wales) and Jago (Cornwall). The spread of the name may be a consequence of international pilgrimages to the shrine of James the Great in Santiago de Compostella in Spain, popular since the Middle Ages.

Several members of British and Scottish royalty bore the name, including James II, who effectively lost his crown at the Irish Battle of the Boyne (1690), and his son, James Edward, long-term pretender to the English throne.

Jamestown, on the river James in Virginia, was the site of the first permanent British settlement in America (1607) and the first legislative assembly in the New World (1619).

Our story is inspired by the Biblical James who lived on the shores of

Lake Galilee in modern day Palestine. The lake is in a deep recess almost 200 metres below sea level and surrounded by high hills. Its geography makes the area prone to fierce localised storms, which arise without notice.

James was an apostle of Jesus and twin brother of John. After Jesus's death, James, known as the Elder or Great, actively promoted the Christian faith and was executed because of this in the reign of Herod Agrippa I. A second apostle, James (the Younger), is referred to without detail in the Bible.

James the Just was a sibling or half brother of Jesus. He is believed to be author of the Letter of James which says that faith must be matched by action. It became a type of charter for Christian Socialism in the early 20th century. He is recorded as being stoned to death during anti-Christian purges in AD 62.

Biblical references: Matthew 4:21ff, 13:55, 17:1ff; Mark 5:37, 10:35ff; Acts 12:2, 12:17, Corinthians 15:7 and Letter of James.

Once there was a boy called James. On one side of his house were great mountains and on the other side a great lake.

The lake was full of every type of fish. There were silver and blue fish, fat fish and flat fish, fish with strange faces and fish with long tails. Often James's dad, who was a fisherman, would show James new types of fish which he had never seen before.

James liked to help prepare the boat and nets. He liked to count how many boxes of fish had been caught. He was very happy when his dad's boat caught the most fish.

James really wanted to go fishing, but he was never allowed. "Sometimes a very strong wind from the mountains causes a storm on the lake. It is too dangerous for a young boy," his dad always said. James would look sad and then his dad would laugh: "When you are older you can come."

"Am I old enough today?" James asked each morning. "When I am I will catch as many fish as you." Still his dad smiled and said no.

Then one day James had a clever idea. He hid under the fishing nets in his dad's boat, and waited. The day was sunny and hot but he put on lots of warm clothes because it gets cold when the sun sets. He would go fishing tonight. James imagined the largest catch ever!

Soon all the fishermen got into the boat. They sailed far out into the lake.

James could not resist looking out from under the fishing net. What a great adventure! He saw flying fish soaring through the air. He saw giant storks soaring in the sky. He leaned out too far and fell into the box where his dad stored the fish. When he climbed out he had a smelly fish tail stuck in his ear and fish bones in his hair.

Soon the fishermen came to cast their nets in the water.

What a surprise they got to find James hiding underneath

but the boat was too far out in the lake to bring him home.

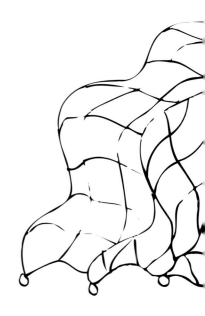

They had just cast their nets on the lake when suddenly the wind began to blow. The boat began to sway as the storm grew fiercer. The fishermen tried to pull in the nets and head for home.

Thunder roared, lightning flashed across the sky. Their clothes were soaked with rain. James was very frightened. He watched his dad working very hard to keep the boat afloat and steer it home. James was not strong enough to help.

Just as quickly the storm passed over and the sea was calm again. The nets, however, had been washed away by the wind and waves.

Then his dad spoke to James. "That was one of the worst storms I have ever seen. I am very cross that you disobeyed me but very happy that we are all safe and well."

He was feeling cold and tired. He had not expected such a scary adventure. He went home to a warm drink and some bread for breakfast.

James didn't ask to go fishing for a long time after that. He knew his dad would tell him when it really was safe for him to go on the lake. He had learned that it is always best to listen to your parents' advice.

What's in a name?

Usually centuries of history, religious or legendary tradition.

The main source of names is in religious history, in the names of saints (Catherine) and, post Reformation, in the *Bible* and *Old Testament* in particular (Sarah and Adam). The *Koran* provides additional perspective on many of these names.

Names from Celtic legend, like Conor, have recently gained increased attention internationally.

Another source is classical, from pagan, royal or literary figures, e.g. Lawrence (Latin) and Chloe (Greek literature). Historical figures, such as Victoria, also provide a rich source.

Then there's Jack! It probably deserves a category all of its own having appeared from nowhere - but perhaps from Jankin, a version of John - to become the ubiquitous name in fairy tales and now a highly popular first name.

Recently parents have become much more adventurous. This follows the decrease in family and religious bonds that resulted in names passing from generation to generation. Increased access to other cultures has led to 'name globalisation', with names like Tanya, Brooklyn and Chelsea now more popular.

Other names recall a particular individual or event. The *Bible* and *Koran* name, Aron, received a new lease of life - and spelling - from Elvis Aaron Presley. Jack